IN THE
VICTORIAN
KITCHEN

A BOOK OF DAYS
Compiled by
J A N E   P E T T I G R E W

A Bulfinch Press Book
Little, Brown and Company
Boston · Toronto · London

First Edition

ISBN 0-8212-1804-2
A CIP catalogue record for this book
is available from the British Library.

Designed by The Image
Typeset by DP Photosetting, Aylesbury, Bucks

Published simultaneously in the United States of
America by Bulfinch Press, an imprint and
trademark of Little, Brown and Company (Inc.),
in Great Britain by Little, Brown and Company (UK) Ltd
and in Canada by Little, Brown and Company (Canada) Limited.

PRINTED IN SPAIN

∞ INTRODUCTION ∞

When Victoria became queen in 1837, Britain was in the early stages of a period of ever-accelerating change, during which the life-style of many thousands of people was revolutionized. For some the quality of life had become worse as many country dwellers, forced out of their small-holdings by the land enclosure legislation of the previous century, moved into the cities in the hope of finding work. They often found themselves living in extreme poverty in filthy slums with insanitary water supplies. Cooking facilities were very basic and food in short supply. For those rural families who still had work, life in their one-roomed cottages was reasonably comfortable, and they, at least, were able to produce a large proportion of food for themselves. Meals were prepared in a large iron pot slung over the open wood or coal fire in a room that served as kitchen, dining room, living room and bedroom, sometimes for as many as three generations of one family.

However, it was the growing middle classes who benefitted most from the industrial and commercial developments of the age. As their wealth grew, they moved into larger houses and employed more servants to carry out every possible task for them in the kitchen and around the rest of the house. Even a humble school-teacher or shopkeeper could afford to employ at least one general servant to scrub, clean, wash, cook and serve food. A family which started with one servant soon found that an increase in earnings allowed an increase in staff to include housemaids, parlourmaids, a butler, footmen, a governess, nursemaids and gardeners as well as extra kitchen maids, a cook and a housekeeper. It

Cocoa, introduced in 1886, was popular as an alternative to tea and coffee at breakfast, and as a warming evening beverage.

is easy to romanticize about the life of both family and servants of that period, and certainly advertisements and trade cards of the time show healthy, rosy-cheeked, smiling servants cleaning very shiny pots, baking perfect cakes and pastries, and seemingly enjoying their daily work. However, the truth is rather different. Admittedly servants were probably much better off in private houses than they would have been in factories, mines or living as one of the urban unemployed, but life below stairs was an endless round of harsh work. All the jobs that we carry out today with the aid of electricity and labour-saving devices, were done by hand – often with no running water and no gadgets. In many houses water had to be carried from pumps, wells, rivers and streams. Water for laundry, bathing and dish-washing had to be heated and carried to different parts of the house. An increase in the use of coal meant that there was dust everywhere, and the list of cleaning and polishing tasks was endless. Cooking on an open fire meant that pots and pans were coated with soot which had to be brushed off before the washing up could be done, and there were no patent washing-up soaps or wash-ing powders to help disperse the grease. Soda was used instead, and servants' hands were usually red and chapped.

The introduction of the closed range into most houses meant that kitchen work became much cleaner and cooler, and cooking pots were not quite so grimy, but the range was a "black monster" which had to be cleaned out, re-lit, polished and blackleaded every morning before breakfast in order to make it presentable, and the flues had to be kept free of soot. As the century progressed and the middle classes grew even wealthier, so they acquired more possessions – more silver needed cleaning, more dresses had to be washed, starched and ironed, more furniture had to be polished and more cooking equipment had to be scrubbed and scoured. The more affluent lifestyle also meant more lavish dinner parties. Victorian dinners could include up to seven courses, and the various dishes for each course had to be ready at the right moment and be beautifully decorated and presented. This meant hours of work in the kitchen, and a great deal of running up and down stairs during the meal. Kitchens were often set away from the main house or deep in the basement, and hot dishes carried along draughty corridors, and up cold flights of stairs did not stay hot for very long.

Changes in kitchen equipment did, in many cases, help to make the servants' lives easier. The improvements in plumbing and sanitation meant that tapped hot and cold water were more readily available, and that slop buckets no longer had to be carried downstairs every morning to be emp-tied. Patent soaps and polishes helped with some of the cleaning tasks and the development of cast iron brought all sorts of equipment which made such jobs as polishing knives, chopping up meat – or even squeezing lemons – much easier. However, the vast armies of servants, many of whom were under fifteen years old, did still have to work extremely hard and for very long hours.

The supply and variety of food in Victorian kitchens improved greatly during the second half of the century, thanks largely to improved distri-bution by the railways, and to new canning and chilling processes. Housewives who had little or no help in the kitchen could easily buy commer-cially baked cakes, good quality flour for baking, fresher milk, tinned meats, fruits and vegetables, gravy and soup concentrates, jelly powders and many more products which made cooking quicker and easier. Until the wider use of gas and electric cookers after the First World War, how-ever, cooking methods and the work carried out in the kitchen remained unchanged through the second half of Victoria's reign.

Oxo was launched in 1900 and quickly became one of the favourite ingredients for soups and sauces.

❧ J A N U A R Y ❧

1

2

3

4

5

6

7

GOING INTO SERVICE

A young girl was very often found her first domestic placing at the age of 11 or 12. She had probably left school at 10 or 11 and had already spent a year working with her mother at home. The mother then found a place for her in the house of a local tradesman or schoolmaster.

There she would work as general maid, kitchen assistant or maid of all work and would receive basic training in domestic duties. From there she would hope to progress to a better position in a larger household. Many girls went to the big cities and found positions through agencies, advertisements, recommendations or at a local hiring fair, where people made themselves available for employment.

In her first position, a young girl would be expected to clean, make beds, black grates, empty slop buckets, scrub floors and steps and help with kitchen work. If she were a maid of all work she would cook and serve the food as well. By the late 1880s, a first salary for such a young girl would be between £8 and £14 a year, and bed and board were free.

How much such a girl learned and how happy she would be depended greatly on the sort of house she was in and on the other staff. Employers could be kind and considerate or cruel and demanding.

A young girl leaves home to take up her first position. She
sadly says goodbye to her family, knowing that she may
not see them for several months.

❧ GOLDEN RULES FOR THE KITCHEN ❧

1
Without cleanliness and punctuality good cooking is impossible.

2
Leave nothing dirty; clean and clear as you go.

3
A time for everything, and everything in time.

4
A good cook wastes nothing.

5
An hour lost in the morning has to be run after all day.

6
Haste without hurry saves worry, fuss and flurry.

7
Stew boiled is stew spoiled.

8
Strong fire for roasting; clear fire for broiling.

9
Wash vegetables in three waters.

10
Boil fish quickly, meat slowly.

MRS ISABELLA BEETON

Mrs Beeton first published her recipes and hints on running a household as monthly instalments in *The Englishwoman's Domestic Magazine*. The first edition of *The Book of Household Management* (the cover is shown below) appeared in 1861. Victorian middle-class ladies were expected to know how to organise their household, hire and train servants, understand food and hygiene, plan meals, bring up children and balance the household accounts. Mrs Beeton, among others, wrote the books that helped to teach them at least some of these skills. The list of rules for the kitchen (shown left) appeared in the 1869 edition.

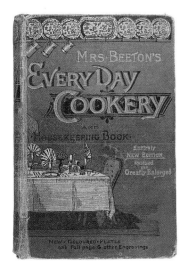

໙ J A N U A R Y ໙

8

9

10

11

12

13

14

๑ J A N U A R Y ๑

15

16

17

18

19

20

21

A PAN FOR EVERY PURPOSE

Victorian cookery books usually gave detailed lists of the equipment needed for cooking and the preparation of food. The illustration shows various pots and pans for different cooking methods.

The stock pot was probably the most important piece of equipment, since a good stock was vital to the preparation of sauces, soups and gravies. Each day a carefully scoured stock pot was placed on the stove and the stock mixture added and simmered for several hours. (Stock from the previous day was stored in earthenware jars in the larder.) The braising pan was used for cooking joints of meat on a bed of chopped bacon, beef or veal, onions, carrots, herbs and stock. The boiling pot was used for large joints, hams and puddings. It was usually made of iron and was tinned inside. The double saucepan was very useful for boiling custards and milk and other preparations that were liable to stick. The inner pan was lined with enamel. The digester (in the centre) was an early type of pressure cooker which allowed the cook to prepare large quantities of food economically by simmering over a very low heat. The fricandeau pan with its wire basket was used for frying patties, rissoles, croquettes, fritters and parsley. The salmon, turbot and fish kettles each had a drainer inside to allow the cooked fish to be lifted out and drained without being damaged.

STOCK-POT.

BAIN-MARIE.

STEW-PAN.

BRAIZING PAN.

BLOCK TIN SAUCEPAN.

BOILING-POT.

DOUBLE, OR MILK, SAUCEPAN.

IRON SAUCEPAN, WITH STEAMER.

OMELETTE PAN.

SAUTÉ-PAN.

FRICANDEAU PAN.

PRESERVING PAN AND SPOON.

SALMON KETTLE.

TURBOT KETTLE.

FISH KETTLE.

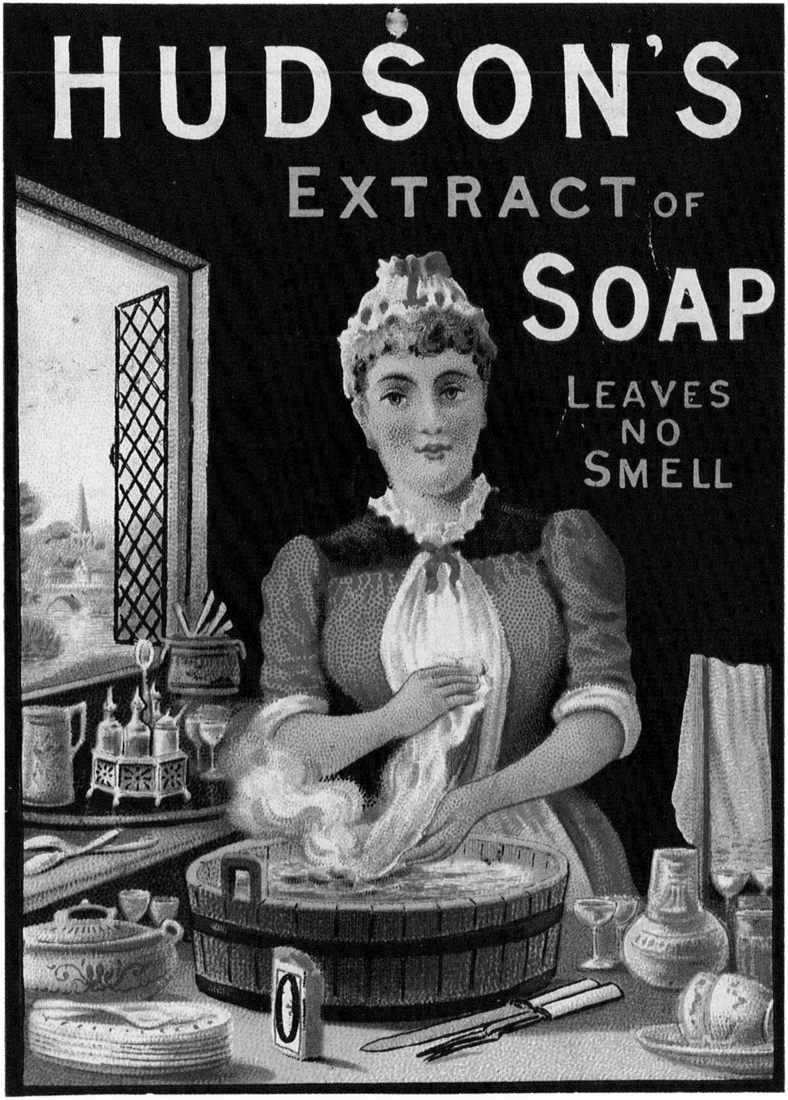
HUDSON'S
EXTRACT OF
SOAP
LEAVES
NO
SMELL

SOAP AND LYE

Since the thirteenth century, soap had been produced commercially, but was also made at home from fat and wood ash. If soap was not available, or in short supply, lye was used instead. Lye was an alkaline liquid made from wood ash collected from furnaces, bread ovens and open fires, and mixed with water. The resulting liquid was strained and poured over and through the dirty fabrics. Other substances such as urine, bran and fowl dung were sometimes added to increase its efficacy.

Until 1853 soap was relatively expensive in Britain because of a tax on it, and some households economized by using a mixture of soap and lye, while others used soap one washday and lye the next. When the tax was dropped that year, the upper classes stopped using lye and used only soap. The middle and lower classes quickly followed suit, and the growth of the soap industry is linked to this period.

Early, commercially-produced soaps often contained soda and were very harsh on the hands.

To make quite sure that the washing came out really clean, the laundry maid would use her knuckles, a scrubbing brush or a washboard with the soap.

ಌ J A N U A R Y ಌ

22

23

24

25

26

27

28

∾ J A N · F E B ∾

29
30
31
1
2
3
4

THE LAST DAYS OF THE STOCK-POT

The stock pot was probably the most important item in the Victorian kitchen, since a good stock was the basis for all soups, stews, gravies and sauces. To make a good stock could take three or four days, and careful guidelines were laid out in all the cookery books of the day. Cooks were advised that the best stock was made from fresh beef, mutton or veal and that fatty or stale meat should be avoided. The meat was browned in a scrupulously clean pan and then other ingredients were gradually added. These included poultry trimmings or bacon rinds, onions, butter, carrots, turnips, celery, mushrooms, a tomato or two, a bunch of herbs, salt, sugar, peppercorns, cloves, blades of mace and water. After three days of gentle simmering and skimming, the stock was worked through a fine muslin cloth or a fine hair-sieve. This could take three or four hours, and the resulting liquid might still need clarifying with egg white, or further skimming to remove the last traces of fat and scum.

During the 1840s in Germany, a concentrated meat extract was perfected by Baron Justus von Liebig. By the 1890s, sales had reached eight million jars a year. Bovril went on sale in 1886 and Oxo was launched in 1900. Although these products made life much easier for the housewife who had little or no help in the kitchen, most professional cooks would have thought them a poor imitation of real stock.

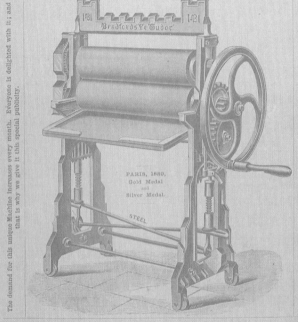

Early mangles were simple wooden machines. Later, cast
iron frames were ornate and gearing control systems
became more complicated and sophisticated.

THE FAMILY WASH

The weekly wash was a complicated and tiring affair. Traditionally, washing was done in cold water, either in a running stream, or, later, in a tub. Hot water had to be heated in a large iron or copper pan on the open kitchen fire, or set over a special furnace in the wash-house or on a brick hearth in the back yard. To heat enough water, the coppers had to be on the fire by 1 or 2 o'clock in the morning. If there was no piped cold water, it had to be fetched from the well, pump or nearby stream. Working class town and village families relied on public wash-houses, which served ten or twelve families and were equipped with a furnace, sink and pump. In the country, the washing was followed by rinsing and beating in cold water and bleaching by laying the clothes out on the grass in the sunlight.

Mangles were first used to smooth and polish dry or damp laundry by passing it over or through rollers. The most effective was the box mangle, invented in the eighteenth century, which used a thick wooden roller around which the linen was wound and a wooden box weighted with stones. The box was moved to and fro across the linen to smooth it. Smaller mangles were invented in the middle of the nineteenth century for both smoothing and wringing water from wet laundry. These were effective and cheap and so were more widely bought than the expensive washing machines of the time.

FEBRUARY

5

6

7

8

9

10

11

❧ F E B R U A R Y ❧

12
13
14
15
16
17
18

THE VALENTINE

When a young girl joined the staff of a large house at the age of 12 or 13 (or even younger), she could expect to work from dawn until very late at night for a few shillings a month, half a day off each week, if she was lucky, and very little other time to herself. If she ever thought of leaving, she knew that she would have to have a good reference from her mistress. Without a "character" she would have little chance of finding another position. So she had very little choice but to stay and endure the routine. Some employers were kind and considerate and treated servants very reasonably. Others were tyrannical and overbearing.

Letters were sometimes opened by the mistress to see if the servants were keeping any secrets and, in most households, no gentlemen callers were allowed unless they were "serious and regular followers", and then only rarely. For many maids the only real contact with the outside world was at the tradesman's entrance. However, most girls did manage to meet somebody suitable, usually on their days off.

This young girl had obviously met someone special and found a quiet corner to read her valentine at leisure.

৵ F E B R U A R Y ৵

19	
20	
21	
22	
23	
24	
25	

SUGAR AND SPICE…

Victorian recipes, such as Mrs Beeton's sherry trifle, ask for pounded sugar. This is because sugar was only available in the form of conical loaves fifteen inches high. This was either broken and sold in chunks by the grocer, or bought whole and broken and used as needed in the home. Chunks were broken off with a small chopper, or nipped off with special tongs, and then pounded with a bottle or a rolling pin and finally sieved to give a fine powder. Almonds came either sweet or bitter and a mixture of the two was often called for.

To make the egg custard, the milk was heated with approximately half a cup of sugar and then allowed to cool. The eggs were whisked and stirred into the cooled milk and the mixture strained into a jug. The jug was then placed in a saucepan of boiling water on the stove, and the custard stirred until it thickened.

The presentation of food was very important to the Victorians, and instructions in recipe books were given for fairly elaborate use of sweetmeats, comfits, angelica, cherries and coloured jellies on the tops of trifles.

VICTORIAN SHERRY TRIFLE

INGREDIENTS

For the whip:
1 pint of double cream
3 oz of pounded sugar
the white of 2 eggs
a small glass of sherry or raisin wine
For the trifle:
1 pint of custard made with 8 eggs to a pint of milk
6 small sponge cakes or 6 slices of sponge cake
12 macaroons
2 dozen ratafias
2 oz of sweet almonds
the grated rind of 1 lemon
a layer of raspberry or strawberry jam
½ pint of sherry or sweet wine
6 tablespoonfuls of brandy

The whip to lay over the top of the trifle should be made the day before it is required for table, as the flavour is better, and it is much more solid than when prepared the same day.

Put into a large bowl the pounded sugar, the whites of the eggs, which should be beaten to a stiff froth, a glass of sherry or sweet wine, and the cream. Whisk those ingredients well in a cool place, and take off the froth with a skimmer as fast as it rises, and put it in a sieve to drain: continue the whisking till there is sufficient of the whip, which must be put away in a cool place to drain.

The next day, place the sponge cakes, macaroons, and the ratafias at the bottom of a trifle dish: pour over them ½ pint of sherry or sweet wine, mixed with 6 tablespoonfuls of brandy, and, should this proportion of wine not be found to be quite sufficient, add a little more, as the cakes should be well soaked. Over the cakes, put the grated lemon-rind, the sweet almonds, blanched and cut into strips, and a layer of raspberry or strawberry jam.

Make a good custard, by recipe, using 8 instead of 5 eggs to the pint of milk, and let this cool a little: then pour it over the cakes etc.

There remains nothing to do now but heap the whip lightly over the top: this should stand as high as possible, and it may be garnished with strips of bright currant jelly, crystallised sweetmeats, or flowers: the small coloured comfits are sometimes used for the purpose of garnishing a trifle but they are now considered rather old-fashioned.

GEO. SALTER & CO.

Household Specialities.

SLICING MACHINE.

For Slicing Cucumbers, Beet, &c. An ordinary
table knife is used.
Price (without knife) 3 each.

HUGHES PATENT
FOUNTAIN
CLOTHES WASHER

WASHING MACHINE.

Made of Zinc. Simple and perfect in working. No
Brushing or scrubbing needed.
Price 4/ to 8/ each.

POTATO CHIP MACHINE.

A movement of the handle makes the
Potatoes into chips ready for cooking.
Price 3/3 each.
Larger size, with spring at back to
raise handle, 5/- each.

LEMON SQUEEZER.

Made in Cast Iron. The Cup is lined
with Enamel, which is specially prepared to resist acid. Price 4/6 each.

BOX IRON.

Price, with Lifter and Two Heaters, from 1/9 each.

MEAT MINCER.

The inside of the Machine is coated with white
Enamel. All the Cutters are steel.
No. 1, price 8/ each.

ROLLER LOCK.

Price 4/ each.

AUTOMATIC INKSTAND.

For Black, Red, and Copying Ink. The opening of one
lid closes another.
Price 3/6 and 4/6 each.

BIGGS' PATENT
TUBULAR MORTICE LOCK

The Best Mortice Lock in the World.
It is made of brass, is cheap, and easily
fitted.
Price, 6-in. (2 levers), 5/ each.
   ,,   4½-in.   ,,   4/6 ,,

GOODS SUPPLIED THROUGH FACTORS AND MERCHANTS.

WEST BROMWICH

HOUSEHOLD SPECIALITIES

From the middle of the nineteenth century, manufacturers of ironmongery started to issue elaborate catalogues of their current products, including an ever-increasing range of household gadgets which were designed to save time and labour in the "modern" kitchen. Some employers considered that the servants did the various jobs adequately and therefore saw no reason to spend more money on extra equipment. But, by the end of the century, most kitchens were equipped with mincers, sausage-makers, bean-slicers, tin-openers, potato-chippers, tongue-presses, egg-toppers, vegetable-slicers, metal lemon-squeezers, ice-cream makers, apple-corers, knife-sharpeners and portable ice-boxes.

However, there was still no electricity and all basic tasks took a long time and a great deal of effort. Eggs and cream still had to be whisked by hand, cake mixtures still had to be beaten – sometimes for up to an hour to incorporate the correct amount of air – and soups and sauces still had to be laboriously worked through a sieve or muslin cloth.

Ironmongers who could not afford to publish detailed catalogues, such as this one from George Salter & Co., relied on travellers to call on small traders.

ᚙ F E B · M A R C H ᚙ

26	
27	
28/29	
1	
2	
3	
4	

Wishing you a Merry Xmas and a happy New Year.

THE AGE OF REFINEMENT

Until 1861, wheat flour for bread-making and other baking was milled when needed as it did not keep well. This was because it contained the wheatgerm as well as a certain amount of bran and therefore quickly went rancid. In 1861 roller mills were introduced to give a refined white flour that no longer contained the wheatgerm or the bran. Both were discarded in the milling process. The resulting flour gave a whiter, spongier bread that kept better and produced lighter cakes and pastry. Nutritionists advised that the loss of the bran and the wheatgerm would have a bad effect on the digestive system, but the lighter, whiter flour became increasingly popular. To enhance the whiteness some bakers added alum, chalk or even ground bones. These also helped to make the flour keep well.

Home baking was an important part of

Coombs, McDougalls and similar companies advertised "aerated" flours that were light, dry and sifted but soda or pearl-ash (partly purified potassium carbonate) was still needed in recipes for cakes and puddings that needed a raising agent.

Victorian cookery as mass-produced cakes did not become generally available until the later part of the century, although biscuits were easily purchased and very popular. As far as cakes were concerned, "professed" cooks preferred to make their own.

Recipes gave clear details as to the quantities of ingredients, but the instructions about oven temperatures and cooking times were much more vague and haphazard than today. The heat of the range was much less easy to control than in today's ovens, and the complicated system of flues and dampers did not guarantee that the correct temperature would be achieved. When baking pastry, cooks were advised to place a small piece of pastry into the oven first to test whether the oven was "heated to the proper degree".

❧ M A R C H ❧

5
6
7
8
9
10
11

COOKING AT THE OPEN FIRE

Before the development of the kitchen range, the most common method of cooking was on an open fire which burned in a cradle-like grate made of horizontal iron bars fixed to four strong legs. The grate was fairly shallow from front to back but high and wide at the front, to make it suitable for spit-roasting. Most food, however, was prepared in a big black iron pot suspended from inside the chimney-piece. Everything was cooked in the pot at the same time: meat, vegetables and dumplings for the main course; and a suet pudding rolled up securely in a floured linen bag, boiling away with the savouries. Baking was done on a griddle or bakestone, or alternatively, the iron pot was detached from its hook and turned upside down over a heated stone. This method of cooking continued, in some places, well into the twentieth century. There were disadvantages to the system: the kitchen was often very hot and smoky; soot could tumble down the chimney at any time and fall straight into the pot, ruining the day's food; and if the pot boiled over it could put out the fire.

With the introduction of the chimney in the sixteenth century, the fire moved from the centre of the room into a wide hearth against the wall. An iron pot suspended over the fire was used to cook most of the family's food.

With mechanical cooling and fast distribution by rail, milk
arrived clean and fresh in churns or bottles, at the
kitchen door.

THE MILKMAN ON HIS ROUNDS

Until the 1860s, town milk was supplied by local cow men. Originally, the cows were kept in parkland or open spaces, but as building increased, open spaces became less accessible and the cows had to be kept in unpleasant, unhealthy sheds off the streets. The animals were badly fed and often sick, and so the milk they gave was thin and watery. Unscrupulous cow men would add hot water and tell the customers that it was warm from the cow.

The buckets in which the milk was carried from door to door were open to dirt and germs. However, the milk was at least fresh, unlike the milk brought in from the countryside which had turned by the time it reached the customer's kitchen. By the end of the 1860s, a mechanical cooler had been introduced which helped to ensure that fresh milk, quickly cooled and brought into the cities by rail, was fit to drink. Pasteurisation was also becoming common, and dairies gradually turned into controlled, hygienic factories where temperature, cream content and yield were carefully measured.

∾ M A R C H ∾

12

13

14

15

16

17

18

∾ M A R C H ∾

19

20

21

22

23

24

25

LEAD KINDLY LIGHT

Until the early part of the twentieth century many houses were still lit by candles and oil-lamps. In some country areas, electricity did not reach villages until the 1920s. In other cases, householders could not, or would not, have electricity installed. So the family lived and the servants worked by candle and lamplight. Employers kept a watchful eye on the supply of candles, sometimes rationing the servants to one candle a week each to light their bedrooms. Servants often rose in the dark and had to carry out the first tasks of the day – sweeping, scrubbing, cleaning fire-grates – by the light of a single candle. Even when electricity was installed, the maid's bedroom was often not connected to the supply and she continued to rise and go to bed by candlelight. Some people believed that the wide arc of light thrown off by an oil lamp was not necessary in bedrooms, and also continued to use only candles.

Although gas lighting had become available at the beginning of the nineteenth century it was not considered satisfactory for domestic purposes. Oil lamps were the most popular form of lighting for the home and most households owned a variety of portable hand lamps, suspension, table and standard lamps, hanging lanterns, bracket lamps and night lights. Until the 1850s and 60s, they burnt colza oil made from rapeseed, or whale oil. These were later replaced by paraffin made from mineral oils.

Even after the introduction of gas and electricity, many
people relied on candles to light their homes.

VEGETABLES IN SEASON

Vegetable	Best and cheapest
Asparagus	April and May
	1½d* to 2d per lb
Beans – French	Sept and Oct
	2d to 4d per lb
– Runner (kidney)	Aug and Sept
	2d to 4d per lb
Brussels sprouts	April
	1d to 2d per lb
Cabbages	Spring and Summer
	1d to 2d each
Carrots	Autumn
	4d to 6d a bunch
Cauliflower	July
	2d to 6d each
Leeks	Oct to end Nov
	4d to 6d a bundle
Lettuces	July and Aug
	1d to 2d each
Mushrooms	Sept and Oct
	4d to 6d per pint
Peas	July and Aug
	6d to 2s per peck†
Potatoes	Autumn
	1d per lb
Spinach	Summer
	2d to 4d per lb
Tomatoes	Sept to Oct
	4d to 8d per lb

* d was the symbol for the penny before British currency was decimalized in February 1971.

† a peck is a volume measure for dry goods and is equal to 2 gallons.

∾ MARCH · APRIL ∾

26

27

28

29

30

31

1

EASTER CAKE

INGREDIENTS

¾ lb of flour
8 oz of butter
5 oz of castor sugar
3 oz of currants
½ teaspoonful of cream of tartar
¼ teaspoonful of bicarbonate of soda
a pinch of salt
1 egg

This late-Victorian recipe is from Florence White's *Good Things in England* and takes 10–15 minutes to prepare.

Rub the butter quickly and lightly into the flour.

Add the sugar and currants, cream of tartar and bicarbonate of soda and salt.

Beat the egg and then mix it in with the flour, using a knife.

Gather the mixture into one piece. Turn out on to a floured board and roll out thinly, about ⅛ inch thick. Then cut out with a round, fluted cutter.

Lay on a greased and floured baking tin and bake in a moderately hot oven 10 or 15 minues.

Take out, sprinkle with castor sugar, and lay on a sieve to cool.

Note: These cakes must be watched carefully while baking as they catch easily, and should only be lightly browned.

THE WEEKLY BAKE

In country kitchens baking was done once a week. The bread oven was built into the chimney and had a small metal door. The oven was heated by means of a fire of brushwood and faggots which was allowed to burn inside the closed, dome-shaped oven. The embers were spread around inside to ensure an even heat throughout, and when the fire had burned down, the ashes were raked out. The oven retained its heat for twenty-four hours and this was enough to cook the family bread and cakes. The bread went in first, placed carefully with a flat wooden implement called a peel. Once the bread was cooked, the cakes, pies and biscuits went in. These were an extra treat and were usually baked for special occasions such as Easter, Saints' days, birthdays and Christmas. Recipes for Easter cakes varied slightly from region to region. Some included brandy and spices. Little cheesecakes and egg custards were also baked for the Easter celebrations.

Several cake and biscuit manufacturers began to offer a wide range of fancy goods in the 1840s and 50s, but many cooks still preferred to bake their own.

∾ A P R I L ∾

2

3

4

5

6

7

8

❧ A P R I L ❧

9

10

11

12

13

14

15

THE MAID OF ALL WORK

As the only servant in a lower middle-class family, the maid of all work often led a sad and solitary life. She was a general servant, found only in the smallest households, employed by people only a step above her on the social scale. Her salary was between £5 and £10 a year and she was allowed only two weeks holiday a year, sometimes a half day on Sundays and perhaps an evening off during the week. She would be busy from 6 o'clock in the morning until 10 or 11 at night. A typical daily routine might be as follows: cleaning out the range and lighting the fire; emptying the soot; sweeping and dusting the dining and living rooms and hall before breakfast; laying, cooking and serving breakfast; cleaning the boots; making the beds; emptying the slops from the night; clearing and washing up the breakfast dishes; cleaning the silver; getting the dinner; clearing away the dinner dishes; cleaning up the kitchen; cleaning the steps and flag-stones; blackleading the grates and the scraper outside the front door; preparing, serving and clearing away the tea; cleaning the pantry; preparing the food for the evening meal; laying and serving it; washing the door, window sills and sink and putting the supper things ready to take upstairs.

Two maids of all work from neighbouring houses find a brief moment to chat.

❧ A P R I L ❧

16

17

18

19

20

21

22

SMOOTHING AND POLISHING IRONS
The idea of using heat for smoothing fabrics developed in the late sixteenth century. Two main types of iron were manufactured – the box-iron and the sad- or flat-iron. The box-iron had a hollow body into which heated iron slugs were placed through a hinged or sliding top. The laundress needed one iron and two slugs which she heated in the fire. Charcoal irons worked on the same principle, and fumes escaped through holes in the side or through a special funnel. The charcoal was kept alight by swinging the iron back and forth. Other fuels were also used – naphtha irons were developed in America in 1868, paraffin irons in Europe in 1890, petroleum and methylated spirit irons in 1900. Sad-irons were made of solid cast iron, faced with steel, and were used in pairs – one in use and the other being heated. The heating was done in a variety of ways: by being propped in front of an open fire; on a special trivet hung on a metal support on the fire bars; standing on the top of a closed range, well to the back, away from the black lead polish; on a special coal-fired conical stove; or in a hot plate built into the chimney. The first electric irons were produced in America in 1880, but they were cumbersome and rather dangerous.

Silber & Fleming were a reputable iron-monger with premises at Wood Street, London.

IRONS FROM SILBER & FLEMING

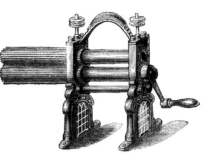

CRIMPING MACHINE

SMOOTHING AND POLISHING IRONS

CHARCOAL OR FUEL IRON

FLUTING OR GOFFERING IRONS

BOX IRON

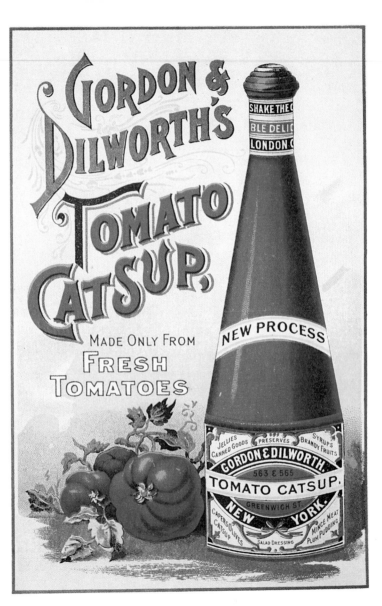

SAUCES, ESSENCES AND KETCHUPS
Prepared sauces played an important part in Victorian cookery. Recipes constantly demanded anchovy sauce, oyster sauce, mushroom or walnut ketchup, Harvey's sauce, chilli vinegar and Worcestershire sauce. They were added to soups and sauces, stews, meat and fish dishes, cheese and egg savouries and pies.

John Burgess was the first company to market anchovy essence in 1760 and launched oyster sauce in the 1820s. Lee and Perrins was established in Worcester in 1823 and in 1837 first marketed their Worcestershire sauce, discovered by accident, when a barrel of ingredients mixed for a client to a Bengali recipe was forgotten and left to ferment. Crosse and Blackwell and other companies quickly followed suit and soon diversified into vinegars, chutneys and pickles. Cookery brought back from the Indian sub-continent was very fashionable, and most cookery books included recipes for curries, pillaus and chutneys to be made at home.

☙ A P R I L ❧

23

24

25

26

27

28

29

∽ A P R I L · M A Y ∽

30

1

2

3

4

5

6

THE HOME DAIRY

Most large houses and farms had a dairy where butter, cream and cheese were made and stored. This was a very cool room or separate building with north-east-facing windows to keep sunlight to a minimum. Surfaces were made of slate or marble and cold water running along a special channel at the edge kept them as cold as possible. The dairy-maid was responsible for receiving the milk pails from the cowman in the morning and evening, and for supplying the family with milk, butter, cream, cheese and buttermilk. Milk which was not immediately needed sat in large basins on the cold slabs for 24–36 hours. The cream was then skimmed off and churned to produce butter. The maid was expected to churn every day in hot weather, and every other day at cooler times of the year. Most were hard at work by 5 o'clock in the morning and spent twenty minutes to half an hour in summer, and longer in winter, making the butter before going on to other jobs. These included scalding and scrubbing out the empty pails, making cheese, feeding left-over buttermilk to the pigs, brushing out the churn and cleaning cream jars.

To make cheese, the milk was heated, rennet was added
and then the liquid was left to curdle in large tubs. The
curds were wrapped in muslin and the whey allowed to
drain out.

The kitchen maid bastes the joint on the bottle-jack while
the cook waits to put some muffins in the oven.

THE BOTTLE JACK

The cast iron range was developed in the eighteenth century as iron foundries increased their ability to produce good quality but cheap castings. In the spaces which had previously existed at either end of the open fire-grate, panels and hobs were installed to allow the use of flat-bottomed pans and kettles, and to provide ovens for baking. Heat from the central fire was directed into the side sections by a system of flues and controlled by dampers. The open fire was still used for roasting, but, since the fire was now narrower, vertical rather than horizontal spits were required. The clockwise bottle-jack was introduced in the 1790s and was the most popular of a variety of jacks patented during the nineteenth century. It suspended and turned the meat in front of the fire. To speed up the process of roasting, it was often used in conjunction with a "hastener" or Dutch oven. These were half-cylinders made of tin that hung from the jack and reflected the heat from the fire back on the meat. A door at the back enabled the cook to check and baste the meat.

There was a gradual change from the open to the closed range. The open fire was covered with a hot plate, and the front usually had moveable panels which could either shut off the fire or expose it to view. This was called a "combination range" or a "kitchener". It was a complicated piece of equipment to maintain and clean, but it was far less hot and dirty than the open range.

∽ M A Y ∽

7

8

9

10

11

12

13

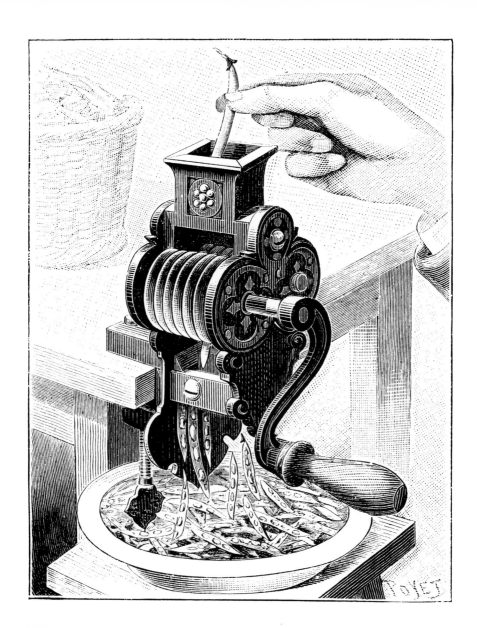

EARLY LABOUR-SAVING DEVICES

In 1865 tinned cast iron and tin plate were combined to make many labour-saving devices. The bean-slicer was just one of the gadgets that began to appear in kitchens in the second half of the century. Cookery books recommended that French and runner beans should be freshly gathered and so young that it was only necessary to top and tail them before boiling in salted water. This would have been easily accomplished on an estate where all the vegetables were home-grown, but most housewives and cooks would have had to buy older, stringier beans which needed more careful preparation. The new utensil would have been a great help in such cases.

Cookery writers also recommended preserving beans by salting them down in large earthenware jars or by bottling them in cold water with a little salt and a pinch of bicarbonate of soda.

Before the introduction of the bean-slicer, the scullery or general kitchen maid would have had the task of preparing and cutting the beans by hand.

ରେ M A Y ରେ

14

15

16

17

18

19

20

∾ M A Y ∾

21

22

23

24

25

26

27

AS KEEN AS MUSTARD

Mustard powder had been available since 1742, from a company called Keen's. Coleman's mustard became available in 1814 when Jeremiah Coleman set up in a mustard and flour mill in Norwich. Mustard tins with highly decorative labels started to appear in the 1850s.

Victorian cookery books gave instructions as to how to mix the powder, and the following different methods were recommended: with water, a little salt and a drop or two of oil to stop the paste from drying; with the addition of a little chilli-vinegar and a pinch of cayenne pepper; with cream or milk to give a milder taste; with the addition of a little sugar to give a gentler flavour.

Mrs Beeton advised that the powder should always be mixed with water that had been boiled and allowed to cool rather than with water straight from the tap which may "cause it to ferment".

Early mustard tins showing the predominant use of yellow.

ᖇᖇ M A Y · J U N E ᖇᖇ

28

29

30

31

1

2

3

AN ARMY OF SERVANTS

Grand houses of the late nineteenth century employed an enormous number of staff. A typical aristocratic home would have had working for them: a steward; a wine butler; several footmen; a master of the servants' hall; several pageboys; a head chef; a second chef; a head baker; a second baker; a head kitchen-maid; various other kitchen-maids; vegetable and scullery maids; a head stillroom maid; a hall porter; two hall boys; kitchen porters; a housekeeper; and various odd-job men as well as the above-stairs staff such as butlers, governesses, ladies' maids, nursery-maids, housemaids and parlour-maids.

Despite the large staff in stately homes, the majority of people in service by the 1870s were working in middle-class houses. The humblest families started with one servant, and as their wealth increased so did the number of staff they hired. A family whose income was £500 a year could afford to employ a cook, a housemaid and a nursemaid.

The kitchen servants lived a totally separate life from the family. They had their own entrances and their own back staircase which connected their sparsely furnished bedrooms to the lower floors where they spent most of their time. Sometimes employers failed to recognize their own servants if they came across them in a corridor or in the grounds. Social barriers were strictly maintained, particularly in middle-class houses.

The staff of a large house pose in crisp caps and aprons
for a group photograph. They are from left to right, with
average earnings in the 1880s: housemaid (£18–£25),
gardener (£15–£20), nursemaid (£8–£14), stillroom maid
(£12–£18), laundry maid (£12–£18), kitchen maid
(£10–£18), butler (£20–£40), lady's maid (£16–£25) and
cook-housekeeper (£20–£50).

THE EVOLUTION OF THE RANGE

The closed range which developed during the nineteenth century had the advantage of allowing several cooking operations to go on at the same time. It was also cleaner and more controllable than the open fire or the open range of previous centuries. However, it was difficult to maintain and clean, and it often did not function properly. The maid had to get up very early to clean and light it, and it required polishing and blackleading every day to keep it presentable. The flues and chimneys had to be regularly cleaned out, and the consumption of coal and the cost of repairs were high.

The next development in the history of cooking was the appearance of the portable range. This cast-iron appliance usually stood on four legs and could be placed in the middle of the room, if necessary, as long as a flue pipe connected it to the chimney or an

Because there was widespread suspicion of gas, it was not until the 1930s that gas cookers became really popular.

Far left a closed range, sometimes also known as a combination range. Above and below left two types of portable range. Right a miracle of modern invention, the gas stove.

outside wall. The stove usually consisted of an oven, a boiler and a hot plate on top. It was more popular in America than in Britain, where the closed range remained the favourite.

The first gas stove was manufactured in 1825, its design based very much on the lines of a coal range. However, it was not until the 1880s that it became at all popular. People believed that the gas contained poison which would affect the food. Their dislike of the smell, and

their suspicions about its safety, did not fade until the 1890s when the ventilation and construction of stoves improved.

The Great Exhibition of 1891 publicized electric cooking, and in 1894 the City of London Electric Lighting Company held an "all-electric" banquet

for 120 guests. The supply of electricity was not widely available, however, and the cookers were expensive, so the spread of electric cooking was very slow. It was not until the 1930s that gas and electric cookers became affordable and acceptable alternatives to the range.

EDWARDS' Desiccated Soups

SOLD EVERYWHERE

In Quarter, Half & One Pound Canisters & One Ounce Packets.

A Book containing 100 Recipes for the use of our Soups sent Gratis and Post Free on application

FREDK. KING & CO. LTD.,

26, Waring Street, BELFAST, and 3 to 6 Camomile Street, LONDON.

THE DESICCATED SOUP

Soup was served either as the main dish of a light meal or as the first of six or seven courses at a dinner party. Most self-respecting cooks would not have resorted to "desiccated" soups. They believed that the basis for a good soup was a carefully prepared stock to which vegetables, meat or fish were added. The gentle simmering or stewing in a closed pan could take four to six hours and was better done the day before it was needed. The secret was to achieve a balance of ingredients so that the flavours did not overwhelm each other. Clear soups had to be absolutely clear and were continuously skimmed to remove all traces of scum. Other soups were thickened with mashed potato, arrowroot, bread raspings, flour and butter, barley, rice, oatmeal or isinglass (an ingredient – similar to gelatine – made from sturgeons' bladders). Sometimes boiled beef was pulped and sieved and added to give extra flavour. Mrs Beeton also recommended careful use of wine and ready-made sauces such as Harvey's sauce, mushroom ketchup or tomato sauce.

Busy housewives who had little experience in the kitchen were grateful for the ease and speed with which dried soup mixtures could be prepared.

৯২ J U N E ৯২

4

5

6

7

8

9

10

∾ J U N E ∾

11
12
13
14
15
16
17

CLEANING AND POLISHING KNIVES

The correct way to clean knives was with an India-rubber and a buff leather knife-board and knife polish shaken out of the top of a drum like those in the picture. The polish was made from finely ground emery and was manufactured by the companies which produced other household polishes and cleaning products. In a large household the butler was responsible for cleaning the knives, and if there was no butler, the scullery- or kitchen-maid was expected to carry out the laborious work. The invention of the knife-cleaning machine helped to cut down the amount of time and energy needed to keep the knife blades smooth and shiny, but when the machines were first invented some families were reluctant to spend money on a gadget when the servants did the job perfectly well. By the end of the century, however, most large households possessed such a machine.

Knife-cleaning machines were designed to be used with patent knife polishes.

THE SCULLERY-MAID

The scullery-maid or general kitchen-maid was responsible for preparing all the vegetables. In all but the very grand houses, there was often no running water or fancy equipment, and potatoes were peeled and other vegetables prepared at the side of a stream or river, or sitting in the backyard with a bowl of water. In houses with running water and a good supply of equipment, the maids still spent an enormous amount of time preparing the vast quantities of food needed for dinner parties. As many as six or seven courses were sent up to the dining table and this meant hours of work in the kitchen during the day. The scullery maid had to work such things as spinach, soups, sauces and chicken-meat through a sieve or muslin, and her other jobs involved washing up greasy pots and pans and cooking utensils, often in cold water with none of the soaps and liquids we take for granted today. She had to wash out cloths in which greasy puddings had been boiled, and generally do all the harder, rougher work in the kitchen.

Preparing the vegetables was a relatively easy job, and it gave the chance to sit down and rest the legs for a while.

♥ J U N E ♥

18

19

20

21

22

23

24

❧ J U N E • J U L Y ❧

25

26

27

28

29

30

1

VICTORIAN CLEANING WISDOM

Many other substances, apart from soap, were used to wash fabrics and to remove stains. Silks were cleaned with starchy water made by soaking raw, grated potatoes in cold water; chintz was sponged with boiled bran; woollens were washed in a mixture made by boiling clean horse hoof parings or with sorrel juice; carpets were cleaned with dry snow and fresh grass clippings. Grease and oil were removed with turpentine and an absorbent powder such as ground sheep's trotters, chalk, pipe clay or fuller's earth (hydrous silicate of alumina). Wax was lifted with a piece of hot coal wrapped in linen or brown paper; ink stains were removed with lemon or onion juice. Wine or vinegar disappeared with the application of warm cow's milk, and fruit stains were rubbed with butter and washed in hot milk. Silk, gold and silver fabrics were rubbed with stale bread or bran. Most housewives had their own special recipes for stain removal, and cookery books usually contained several pages of instructions for various fabric cleaning tasks.

In good weather the clean washing was carried outside to be hung on hedgerows or on a line to dry. On wet days it was dried in front of the fire.

Working class country families enjoyed a far better quality
of life than city dwellers, with plenty to eat and an
abundance of clean, fresh air.

THE HEART OF THE HOME

By the middle of the nineteenth century, poorer famlies began to eat slightly better than they had done in the earlier part of the century. The variety and quality of food in the cities began to improve, due mainly to the distribution by rail of fresh and bulk-processed foods.

Country folk also began to eat better and could generally afford at least one large hot meal, other than soup, a week. Women generally knew only what they had learnt from their mothers, or from their years in service, about cooking and housekeeping. Family meals were usually vegetable stews and broths with dumplings or potatoes, all cooked in one pot that was suspended over the open fire.

The fire was never allowed to go out and the glowing embers were covered at night with a "couvre-feu" (from which we get the word curfew), made from sheet brass or copper, which reduce ventilation. The fire was brought back to life the next morning with the assistance of bellows (see below). There are tales of families who kept the kitchen fire alight for over a century.

⋙ J U L Y ⋘

2

3

4

5

6

7

8

৵৹ J U L Y ৵৹

9

10

11

12

13

14

15

PASCALLS PATENT JELLY

At the Great Exhibition of 1851, held in the Crystal Palace, sweet moulded jellies (gelatins) were the most popular dessert served in the refreshment rooms. This started a new fashion, and jellies and creams became extremely popular. Concentrated powders from Pascalls and many other companies made the preparation of elaborate moulded puddings much easier.

Before these had become available, blancmanges were made by dissolving gelatine in boiling milk then straining the mixture through a flannel straining bag. The liquid was then poured into a mould which was placed in an "ice-cave", or early refrigerator, to set. Jellies were made with gelatine or isinglass.

Gelatine (made from animal tissue) was said by Liebig, inventor of concentrated meat extract, to excite nausea, and, since it contained no nutritive value, it reduced the nutritive value of the food by rendering it inferior in quality. Isinglass was a corruption from the Dutch word "luisenblas" meaning sturgeon's bladder from which it was made. It varied in strength and quality, and making a jelly could be a risky affair as it was difficult to gauge the correct proportions. More was needed for large jellies or for moulds that were not to be chilled or frozen.

Life was much easier when all the cook had to do was open a packet of Pascall's and follow the instructions.

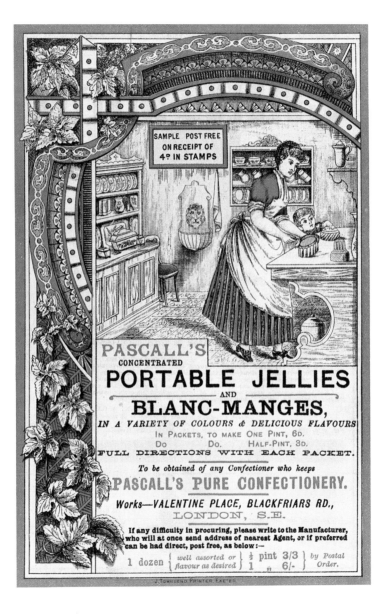

SAMPLE POST FREE
ON RECEIPT OF
4ᴅ IN STAMPS

PASCALL'S
CONCENTRATED
PORTABLE JELLIES
AND
BLANC-MANGES,

IN A VARIETY OF COLOURS & DELICIOUS FLAVOURS

In Packets, to make One Pint, 6ᴅ.
Do   Do.   Half-Pint, 3ᴅ.

FULL DIRECTIONS WITH EACH PACKET.

To be obtained of any Confectioner who keeps

PASCALL'S PURE CONFECTIONERY.

Works—VALENTINE PLACE, BLACKFRIARS RD.,
LONDON, S.E.

If any difficulty in procuring, please write to the Manufacturer, who will at once send address of nearest Agent, or if preferred can be had direct, post free, as below:—

| 1 dozen | { well assorted or flavour as desired } | ½ pint 3/3 | } by Postal |
| | | 1 „ 6/- | Order. |

๛ J U L Y ๛

16

17

18

19

20

21

22

SPICK AND SPAN

Brooke offered for purchase a soap that they claimed would clean just about everything except clothes. The increase in the use of coal throughout the nineteenth century meant an increase in dust and grime, and an increase in affluence meant that each household possessed more items that needed cleaning. As a result there was a long list of cleaning tasks to be carried out by the various maids. Before patent products appeared on the market, polishes and other cleaning fluids were made at home: a paste of lemon juice and whitening was used for ivory piano keys; silver-sand and vinegar were used for scouring copper pans; melted beeswax or candle ends and turpentine were mixed to make floor polish; and furniture was polished with a mixture of methylated spirits, linseed oil and white wax. Soda was used for floors, tables and cooking utensils; paraffin cleaned windows; brass was cleaned with boiling vinegar or crushed rhubarb leaves; and pewter was polished with a paste of fine bathbrick dust and oil. Even tooth powders were mixed from bole (a friable, earthy red clay), armoniac, tree bark, camphor and powdered myrrh.

When the silver had been cleaned, it was returned to its usual place in the Plate Room, next to the Butler's Pantry.

BROOKE'S SOAP
MONKEY BRAND
WON'T WASH CLOTHES
BROOKE'S
C. Lillie
MAKES BRIGHT REFLECTIONS

Cook and two kitchen-maids preparing
dinner on the typical pine table in the
middle of a large country kitchen.

EMPRESS OF THE KITCHEN

Good cooks were notoriously difficult to find and cartoons appeared constantly in Punch and other weekly magazines to highlight the problems employers had with cooks who couldn't cook, who answered back to the mistress of the house, who saw the kitchen as their empire and ruled fiercely over all who worked in it, and who refused to listen to instructions or advice. Sometimes employers and staff alike were terrified of this kind of cook. Housekeepers could be just as intimidating and the sound of the swish of her or cook's skirts and the jangling of the storeroom keys that hung at her side on a long chain set all but the bravest maids trembling. Cooks also had a habit of walking out at a moment's notice, leaving everyone wondering how they were going to cope, but maids and ladies of the house just had to manage as best they could until a new cook was found. However, some houses were lucky and found cooks who stayed for years and almost became like one of the family.

JULY

23

24

25

26

27

28

29

∝ J U L Y · A U G ∝

30
31
1
2
3
4
5

SPIT AND POLISH

Patent stove polishes became available in the 1880s, and may have helped a little in this onerous daily task, although many successful cleaning mixtures were made at home. For the weekly cleaning of the table silver a mixture of hartshorn powder, water and alcohol was used and obstinate stains were removed with ammonia or methylated spirits. Soft rags for rubbing over the silver during the week were made by boiling old cotton stocking tops in a mixture of fresh milk and hartshorn powder. As families grew wealthier, so they acquried more quality china, glass and silver. A typical collection of silver would have included heavy candelabra, fruit bowls, flower baskets, finger-bowls, wine-stands, decanter holders, platters, teapots, cake-stands and vases.

An imaginative advertisement for stove polish from an American firm, Donaldson Brothers of Five Points, New York.

"LOOK AT THIS PICTURE."

DONALDSON BROTHERS, FIVE POINTS, N.Y.

What, Mary! haven't you got the dinner or even set the table yet? No! we have been trying all the morning to black the st— with that horrid old Polish you bought yesterday. It was put up in the same shape and style as The Rising Sun, but is nothing like it, and is a mean miserable cheat.

"AND THEN ON THIS."

"Ah! my dear, dinner is all ready I see, and I am early too." "Yes! dear we had The Rising Sun Stove Polish" to use to-day. I am sure we can't be happy if you get any other kind. No peddler can ever humbug me again with pastes, and paints in boxes and bottles.

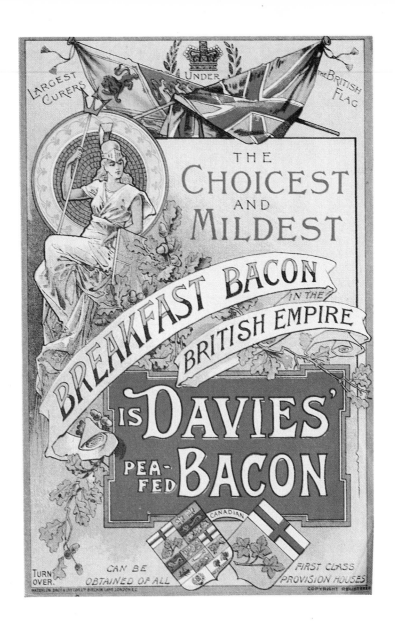

THE BRITISH BREAKFAST

Between 1800 and 1840, it was usual to serve quite a substantial breakfast between 9 and 10 o'clock. Luncheon was a light snack eaten at about 1 o'clock and dinner was at 5 or 6, although this was gradually changing to a later hour.

Between 1840 and 1900 meal times changed and most meals became larger and more elaborate. The urban middle class was becoming richer and families could afford to eat increasingly well.

Breakfast moved forward to 8 o'clock so that the man of the house could eat a hearty meal before setting out for work. A typical Victorian breakfast in a wealthy household consisted of a vast array of hot and cold dishes – a cold joint, game or poultry, game pie, veal and ham pie, cold ham or tongue, hot broiled mackerel, mutton chops, rump steaks, kidneys, sausages, bacon, fried, scrambled, poached or boiled eggs, mushrooms, muffins, toast, butter, marmalade, jam, honey, tea, coffee or cocoa, and sometimes fresh fruit in the summer.

Cooks and kitchen maids would have been working for at least two hours before all this could be sent up to the dining room.

Traditionally, pigs have thrived on all sorts of different foods – acorns, fallen fruit, roots, vegetable and fish refuse. This brand of bacon was from pea-fed pigs.

∽ A U G U S T ∽

6

7

8

9

10

11

12

❧ A U G U S T ❧

13

14

15

16

17

18

19

SPRING CLEANING

Although the daily routine involved a wide range of cleaning tasks around the house, especially in the kitchen which was always kept well and truly scrubbed, major cleaning was often carried out when the family was away. All sorts of different polishes and creams were needed. Maids scurried up and down the stairs with buckets and cans of water to clean blinds, woodwork, ceiling, cupboards and shelves. Carpets were taken up, curtains were taken down and washed, white paintwork was repolished with a special cream, floors were polished and linen was sorted and repaired.

Many of the early patent cleaning products available on
the market were no better than traditional
home-made polishes.

The servants were allowed to receive occasional visitors –
relatives or friends – and they valued the chance for a chat
and a cup of tea together in the servants' hall.

TEA TIME IN THE SERVANTS' HALL

The servants in large houses had their own hall where they ate their meals, relaxed, sewed, knitted and read. The cook and housekeeper had their own rooms but always presided at meal times in the hall. The housekeeper would sit at one end of the table and the butler at the other, and – in some cases – no-one was allowed to speak during the meal. In very grand houses the upper servants – the parlour maids, housemaids, butler and footmen – had a separate room which was referred to as "Pug's Parlour". There could be a great deal of jealousy and snobbery amongst the different levels of servants but everyone was expected to accept the hierarchy and behave accordingly. However, at times when the staff were not required upstairs, it was in the servants' hall that there might be some singing and dancing, a few card games, lively chatter and a bit of fun for the hard-working team.

The servants' hall was always warm as it was near the kitchens and had a fire blazing in the hearth in winter. On the wall was a bell board so that the servants could see immediately if one of the family was ringing so they could respond swiftly. There were sometimes also speaking tubes connecting the hall to the main rooms upstairs.

≈ A U G U S T ≈

20

21

22

23

24

25

26

FREEZING APPARATUS FROM GEORGE KEITH

METAL ICE BOX

WINE FREEZER

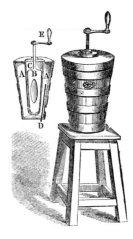

ICE CREAM APPARATUS

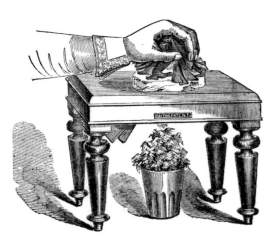

ICE PLANE

ICE SAFE

ICE AND ICE CREAM

All large Victorian houses were equipped with an ice house, and ice cream and fancy iced puddings were extremely popular. Ice had been stored in blocks underground or in well-insulated ice houses since the 1660s, but by 1840 tin- and zinc-lined boxes were becoming popular for use actually in the kitchen or storeroom. These early boxes were packed with ice and the food stood on top. By 1855, ice chests were being manufactured with an aerated top compartment for crushed ice, a drainage system for melted ice water and a lower chilled compartment for the food. Before the invention of ice cream machines, the creamed mixture was poured into moulds surrounded by an ice-packed case. By 1864 machines were being developed which gave a better texture to the ice cream by churning it while it froze. Early models were boxes or pails with a cylinder that was cranked by a handle. Later models, like the one illustrated, had a paddle inside which was rotated by the handle on the top.

This currant and raspberry ice cream recipe is from C E Francatelli's *The Cook's Guide, and Housekeeper's and Butler's Assistant*, published in 1874.

Pick and bruise a pound of redcurrants and half a pound of raspberries, with ten ounces of loaf sugar; stir this in a sugar boiler on the fire until it begins to simmer, and then rub the whole through a hair sieve; mix the pulp with a pint of double cream; mould and freeze the ice.

⊷ A U G · S E P ⊷

27

28

29

30

31

1

2

∞ S E P T E M B E R ∞

3

4

5

6

7

8

9

BAKING A RICH FRUIT CAKE

To make the sort of fruit cake shown in the illustration, hours of preparation were needed. The flavourings, such as lemon or orange rind or nutmeg, had to be grated; the flour sifted to remove the lumps; the butter washed free of salt and squeezed in a muslin cloth to remove any water or buttermilk; and the dried fruit carefully washed, dried and picked over.

First, the currants and sultanas were rubbed with flour to break up the lumps, then the stalks and any grit were removed. They were washed with cold water in a colander, drained, spread out on a soft cloth and gently squeezed to remove the water. They were then spread on a baking tin and dried very slowly in a cool oven.

When dry they were checked again for any remaining stalks and grit, and eventually they were ready to be mixed into the cake or pudding.

Dried egg powders were often kept in the larder in case of emergencies, or for times when new-laid eggs were scarce.

BLACK LEAD AND BOOT POLISH

Before gas and electric cookers were introduced, many houses used coal-fired ranges for all cooking and water heating. The range had to be cleared out, blackleaded and re-lit by 6 o'clock every morning. The daily routine involved removing the fender and fender irons; raking out all the ashes and cinders; throwing on some damp tea leaves to keep the dust down; sifting the cinders; cleaning the flues; removing the grease from the stove with newspaper; polishing the steels with emery paper, bathbrick and paraffin; black-leading the iron parts and polishing them; washing and whitening the hearthstone; then relaying and re-lighting the fire. If the fire was inexpertly lit it would fill the kitchen with smoke, fill the maids eyes with tears and coat the furniture with a layer of dust.

Black lead was used on other grates around the house and a similar routine of raking out and sifting cinders, polishing grates and whitening hearths was carried out by housemaids and maids of all work. The black lead was applied with a soft brush, rubbed vigorously with a harder one and then polished with a cloth. Before commercially produced black lead appeared on the market, blacking for stoves and grates was made with ivory black, treacle, oil, beer and sulphuric acid. Patent pastes, liquids and polishes often incorporated very similar

If manufacturers, such as Nixey's, could persuade people to buy their brand of black lead they stood to make a very healthy profit since every range in every kitchen was polished each morning.

The caption on the poster from which the above illustration is taken read: "When you enter the shop to buy Nixey's black lead, don't be tempted to purchase some other instead."

ingredients and were therefore no more helpful. Reckitt's *Zebra* black lead grate polish, introduced in 1890 seems to have been more effective and labour-saving.

The general servant or maid of all work was responsible for cleaning the master's boots, and sometimes even had to put them on him before he left the house in the morning. If the household employed a house-boy, footboy or hall-boy, it was his job to polish the boots and whiten the tennis shoes.

THE ERA OF STARCH

Early starches were made by boiling hoof-clippings, rice or wheat in water. Later, the most common starch solution was made by soaking grated, raw, old potatoes in cold water to produce a thick paste. In large Victorian households, there was a great deal of starching to be done after the clothes and linens had been washed and bleached. All the tablecloths, napkins, pillow-cases, antimacassars, aprons, caps, collars and shirt-fronts needed stiffening.

Products such as Borax were used for items that needed to be highly starched. Articles that needed only light stiffening were treated with potato starch, or a mixture of salted water and melted white wax. Garments were left to dry after starching and then ironed on the right side. They were sometimes also rubbed over with a smooth stone or the bottom of a bottle to give a very slick finish.

∞ S E P T E M B E R ∞

10

11

12

13

14

15

16

ೞ S E P T E M B E R ೞ

17

18

19

20

21

22

23

WE THANK THEE LORD...

In large houses the servants had their own hall where meals were served and where the hard-working maids and manservants could find a few moments peace and quiet away from their demanding routine. In simpler households, where space did not allow for a servants' hall, family and staff would eat in the same dining room, but at separate tables.

In some homes, servants ate almost as well as the family, enjoying lunch-time left-overs – such as grouse, pheasant, ham or chicken from the family's table – for their evening meal, and hot dinners, specially prepared by the cook, for their midday meal. In other cases the staff were never allowed the more expensive items such as butter, but were expected to work an 18 hour day (or longer) on one meal a day, with bread and dripping or margarine for breakfast and tea. However, servants were generally better fed than the majority of people who lived and worked in the cities. During the first half of the nineteenth century the urban poor lived on a very thin diet of bread, potatoes, scraps of meat and porridge, whereas even servants in a house where no luxuries were allowed ate at least one hot meal of meat and vegetables every day.

The cook, coachman, gardener and general manservant
enjoy a much simpler meal than the family.
Their lunch probably consisted of bread and cheese
and a mug of ale.

This 1867 print shows a mother and her daughter rolling
the pastry for an apple pie in a simple rural kitchen.

MAKING APPLE PIE

Mothers passed their culinary skills and knowledge of housekeeping on to their daughters. The art of pastry making was one of the most important of these skills, since Victorian cookery demanded ingenious uses of different sorts of pastry to make elaborate pie and pâté cases and puddings. Mrs Beeton wrote in her *Book of Household Management* ".... pastry is one of the most important branches of culinary science. It unceasingly occupies itself with ministering pleasure to the sight as well as to the taste, with erecting graceful monuments, miniature fortresses, and all kinds of architectural imitations composed of the sweetest and most agreeable products of all climates and countries."

Cooks were advised to used the best quality and perfectly dry flour, fresh butter washed free of salt and with all the water and buttermilk squeezed out, sweet, fresh lard and beef or veal suet that was free from skin. The pastry should be handled lightly with cool hands on a cool board – for example a marble or slate slab – and in the coolest part of the house.

∾ S E P T E M B E R ∾

24
25
26
27
28
29
30

❧ O C T O B E R ❧

1	
2	
3	
4	
5	
6	
7	

THE COUNTRY HOUSE KITCHEN

In many large town houses, and on most country estates, the kitchens were built in a separate wing to avoid the risk of fire and to keep cooking smells away from the main house. This meant that food had to be carried along draughty corridors, or across courtyards, to the dining rooms. Consquently food was often cold or lukewarm when it was eventually served. In smaller houses the kitchens were in the basements and were often rather dark.

Cookery books gave explicit advice as to how to arrange and equip the kitchens and storerooms, and listed details of size, cost and correct usage of the different pieces of equipment. Householders were advised to ensure that kitchens were large, light, well-ventilated, with high ceilings and a good supply of fuel and water. The centre of the main kitchen was occupied by a large pine or deal table, preferably without flaps, which some considered to be unstable, and, against one wall, a large dresser for storing china and utensils.

In cupboards and on shelves and hooks was arranged a supply of tin-lined copper pans, bowls, whisks, colanders, sieves, moulds, baking-tins, preserving pans, rolling-pins, pastry-jiggers, lemon-squeezers, nutmeg-graters, spice-boxes, butter-pats and curlers, choppers, toasting-forks, skimming- and basting-spoons and every other possible requirement.

The cook of a large country house working in the kitchen
with its typical range of copper pots and pans, gadgets and
useful utensils.

A WELL-STOCKED DRESSER

In early Victorian days, packaged goods were rare. Retailers bought most of their food supplies direct from farmers and manufacturers. Goods were then bought loose from the shops or markets and if they were wrapped at all it was in paper bags, newspaper or tissue supplied by the shopkeeper. Gradually, tins, jars, packets and boxes began to appear, and manufacturers had to be more aware of the way they promoted their products by using attractive packaging. Brand names were established and trade marks were introduced.

By the middle of the century, foreign packaging and labelling was a feature in most grocery shops as, by now, canned and dried foods were being imported to Britain from such places as North America, Africa, the continent and India. Dates arrived from North Africa and muscatel raisins from Malaga in Spain. Preservation of food by drying had been used for centuries but these exotic foods had never been available in Britain. They were brought in for the festive Christmas season and their high cost would have meant that they were seen on the upstairs dining table but not in the servants' hall.

Different products required different types of packaging. Jam was sold in earthenware or glass pots and jars; sweets, custard powders, cocoa and mustards in tins; soups and jellies in packets, but the most common form of packaging was the cardboard box.

❧ O C T O B E R ❧

8

9

10

11

12

13

14

∾ O C T O B E R ∾

15

16

17

18

19

20

21

LAUNDRY GIRLS

Large houses always had separate laundry rooms away from the main house. There was usually a washing house, a bleaching house and an ironing and drying room. The ideal washing house was equipped with a range of wooden tubs, hot and cold water and a boiler or furnace for heating the water. The floor was stone and sloped gently away towards a gutter which was connected with the main drains.

There would be one or more laundry maids, depending on the size of the household, and they were responsible for "washing and getting up" the family linen. The work started at 4 or 5 o'clock in the morning and it took a week to work through all the washing, bleaching, starching and ironing. In smaller households, extra help was hired, or washing was given to the local washerwoman who charged 1d per dozen small items and 2d per dozen larger ones.

In large houses the laundry maids were under the control of the head housemaid. Wealthy families sometimes employed up to four laundry maids to cope with the vast quantities of clothes and linens.

∞ O C T O B E R ∞

22
23
24
25
26
27
28

THE ADVENT OF CANNED GOODS

Canned foods were first produced in Britain by Donkin and Hall at their factory in Bermondsey, London. By 1818 they were turning out cured beef, boiled beef, mutton and vegetable stew, veal, carrots and soups. These goods were more expensive than fresh foods, and at first were only bought by explorers and travellers, or by the navy. By 1830, cans began to appear in grocers' shops, and by 1875 American and Australian canned products were finding a ready market in Victorian Britain.

The early cans were hand-made, but by 1868 a machine method was used. Opening the early cans was a hazardous affair and instructions on products read "Cut round the top near the outer edge with a chisel and hammer". Can-openers (see below) were first introduced in the 1860s for use with tins of corned (bully) beef, which were usually decorated with a bull's head. By the 1890s most middle-class larders would have been well stocked with a variety of canned and packeted foods.

In America, the packaging of fruit and vegetables
was of a very high standard and labels were highly
coloured and very attractive.

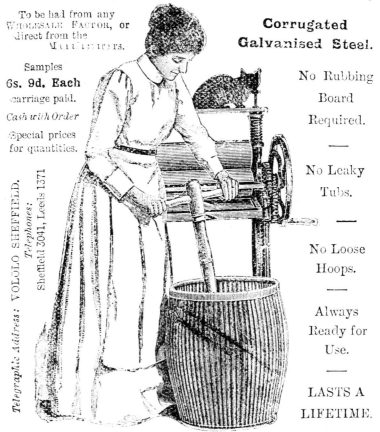

THE DOLLY TUB

Large quantities of washing were done with a dolly tub and dolly peg, posser or punch. Using the dolly peg was strenuous work, requiring a rotating and an up-and-down movement to work the dirt from the fabrics. The dolly was also used to scoop clothes out of water that was too hot to handle. The cone-shaped punch, with its metal base, was designed to agitate clothes by suction. Possers were often home-made from pine, and were used like a dolly, but without the circular movement. Zinc tubs, which were lighter to carry and easier to clean than wooden ones, became available towards the end of the century.

By the 1850s, washing machines that worked on the same principle as a butter churn, began to appear, but they were too expensive for the general market. They also required a supply of hot running water which most houses still did not have. Electric machines did not appear until 1906.

A dolly peg (right), a washing punch and a long-handled posser.

৵ O C T · N O V ৵

29	
30	
31	
1	
2	
3	
4	

❧ N O V E M B E R ❧

5

6

7

8

9

10

11

THE COTTAGE KITCHEN

In the large towns of the nineteenth century, poverty and slum conditions were rife. Thousands of country labourers who had lost their smallholdings in the 18th century under the land enclosure laws had settled in the cities in the hope of finding work.

For those rural cottagers who still had work and a small garden in which to grow vegetables, life was better. The country air was clean, there was access to a clean water supply and they could provide much of their food themselves.

On a salary of £12 a year, a farm foreman would have had a house and garden, a cow, a pig, some hens and an extra allowance from his employer of beer and bread during harvest. In the one-roomed house, the cottager's wife cooked reasonably wholesome meals for the family. She had greens, potatoes, onions and peas from the garden; milk, cheese, cream and butter from the cow; oatmeal from the fields; eggs from the fowls; and, when the pig was killed in the late autumn, a supply of bacon, ham, pork and lard kept them in meat for the winter months. What money was available bought tea, coffee, cocoa, spices, beer, extra meat, soap, candles and clothes.

Many extended families lived, ate and slept in one-roomed houses. All the cooking, washing, ironing and sewing had to be done there and the cottage kitchen was the heart of the family. The fire was never allowed to go out so it was always warm and welcoming inside.

❧ N O V E M B E R ❧

12

| 13 |

| 14 |

| 15 |

| 16 |

| 17 |

| 18 |

THE FISH COURSE

Fish dishes were usually served with soups as the first course of a dinner. These were followed by made-up meat dishes or "entrées", ie roast meats, poultry or game. Next came the "entremets", a selection of vegetable and sweet dishes, and finally the dessert.

Fish was sold from an ice-laden cart in the street. In the 1830s ice-making machines had been invented; the later manufacture (in America) of an ether-compressor made it possible to open an ice factory. Manufactured ice played a large part in the improved fortunes of the fishing industry in the later part of the nineteenth century. Trawlers could travel long distances with fish packed in ice in the hold, and the catch was still fresh when it reached the ports. The fish was then chilled during its journey to the fishmonger and was still in good condition when it was bought by the housewife or cook on the kitchen doorstep. Mrs Beeton wrote of the importance of serving good, fresh fish. She said that "if this important course in a dinner does not give satisfaction, it is rarely that the repast goes off well."

These coloured plates are taken from Mrs Beeton's *Every Day Cookery and Housekeeping Book*, published in 1865. She recommends the Matelotte of crayfish (centre) as "a remarkably pretty dish, which may be served at breakfast, luncheon, dinner, or supper, or part of a second course."

HOT WATER ON TAP

Until the late nineteenth and early twentieth century, many women had to carry the water they needed for cleaning, laundry, food preparation and personal washing from roadside springs, wells and pumps or from a nearby river or stream. Piped water did not become generally available until the early 1900s.

Men rarely fetched water unless they were professional water carriers, so the women had to do it. They carried anything up to six gallons at a time, in hand-held pitchers, cans or barrels, or in larger tubs or buckets on their head. In grand houses, piped water was generally available but, at first, only to the lower floor. So the kitchen, scullery and other basement rooms were supplied, but the servants had to carry hot and cold water to all other parts of the house.

If only cold water was available, it was heated in a large copper on the fire and carried upstairs for baths, washing and cleaning.

By the late 1850s, gas was being used for water heating, but the early geysers were dangerous and often exploded. Towards the end of the century methods and equipment were improving and Ewarts offered a safe and efficient gas water-heating system that would pump hot water to all parts of the house.

⊷ N O V E M B E R ⊷

19

20

21

22

23

24

25

KITCHEN MINCER

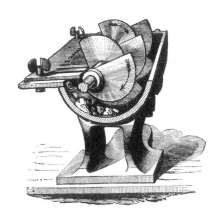

MEAT CUTTER

COMPOUND MINCER AND SAUSAGE FILLER

STANDARD MINCING MACHINE

Sausage-making and mincing machines from the Silber and Fleming catalogue. By the middle of the century the standard mincer consisted of a horizontal cast-iron drum inside which rotated propeller-like blades.

MINCED MUTTON

A true Victorian cook really proved her worth in the kitchen when it came to dishes which used cuts of meat other than straightforward joints which were roasted. It was inevitable, because of the huge amount of food sent up to the dining table in most Victorian households, that a large proportion of food was returned to the kitchen and whatever was left made its way back downstairs and was rehashed into dinners for the servants or into new concoctions for the family. Mincing machines were therefore very useful in shredding the left-overs ready for pies, puddings, rissoles, fritters, toad-in-the-hole, collops, hotchpotch and potted meats.

This recipe for minced mutton comes from C.E. Francatelli's *The Cook's Guide and Housekeeper's and Butler's Assistant*, published in 1874.

Chop the mince very fine, or else cut it up in very thin shreds, and set this aside on a plate, put an ounce of butter, ditto of flour, and a little chopped shallot in a stewpan, and stir this over a very slow fire until it assumes the lightest fawn colour; then moisten with a glass of port, ditto of Harvey (for Harvey's sauce substitute Worcestershire sauce), grated nutmeg and lemon-peel, pepper and salt. Add the minced mutton, a little currant jelly, if suited to taste, and stir all together over the fire until quite hot, and serve with poached eggs on the top, and a border of potato croquettes round the base.

N O V · D E C

26

27

28

29

30

1

2

∞ DECEMBER ∞

3

4

5

6

7

8

9

THE TRADESMAN'S ENTRANCE

Tradesmen called at the side, or back, door of the house with the daily supplies. The butcher had a high dog-cart, the baker carried bread in a large basket covered with a white cloth, the milkman brought the milk in two big churns on the back of a pony-drawn chariot and measured the daily requirement into large jugs. The muffin man carried trays of muffins on his head and walked the streets ringing his bell. The fishmonger pushed an ice-laden cart loaded with hake, cod, salmon, skate, eels, herring, shellfish and even lobsters; and the greengrocer's cart brought fresh fruit and vegetables.

Other salesmen and tinkers arrived with trays of fancy goods – ribbons, lace, sewing notions – or household necessities – string, candles, matches, cleaning products, polishes and the like. Until the coming of the railways in the 1860s, country and town housewives alike had problems in buying what they needed.

With the railways came a wider range of goods including produce from abroad. Fish became more widely available and there was an increase in the variety of fruit and vegetables. The quality of milk also improved as better transportation and mechanical milking made for a cleaner and fresher supply from the farms.

DIRECTION for making quickly.
FOR A BREAKFAST CUP.
Mix a teaspoonful dry with the same bulk of sugar, then pour on boiling water. It is improved by boiling. This Cocoa is perfectly pure.

CADBURY'S COCOA

IS SOLD
ONLY IN TINS
AND PACKETS

TINS AT   PACKETS
9ᵈ 1/-1/6   ·   AT 3ᵈ.
3/- 6/-   6ᵈ

"*Absolutely Pure*
therefore BEST." *The Analyst.*

CADBURY'S COCOA
Absolutely Pure

DIRECTIONS
for making Cocoa
in perfection.

TO MAKE THREE BREAKFAST CUPS.

In a quart jug (with rounded bottom and narrower neck for preference) mix 1½ dessert spoonfuls (¾oz) of **CADBURY'S COCOA** with equal bulk of powdered white sugar and stir to a thin paste with a little boiling water.

Mix in an enamelled saucepan one breakfast cup of milk with two cups of water (cups to be about ¾ full) and boil with care. When on the boil pour this over the contents of the jug and whisk vigorously for a few seconds.

Serve to table without delay.

Following Cadbury's launch of its Cocoa in 1866, Frys introduced a similar product in 1868 and Rowntree's *Elect* cocoa appeared in 1880.

CUPS THAT CHEERED

By the middle of the eighteenth century tea had become Britain's national beverage, but coffee and chocolate were also still extremely popular.

Coffee and cocoa were served as an alternative to tea at breakfast, and cocoa or hot chocolate were often taken late in the evening before retiring. The kitchen- or scullery-maid would have been responsible for grinding coffee beans, as required, in a large wooden or pottery mill.

The preparation of chocolate was more complicated. Until prepared chocolates such as Cadbury's cocoa appeared on the market in 1866, the "nibs" (the crushed cocoa beans) had to be pounded and stewed for hours. When the mixture was cold, the white cocoa butter was removed and the chocolate reboiled with milk and other flavourings such as cinnamon or vanilla. Just before serving, the drink was thickened with beaten eggs. Chocolate powders started to appear towards the end of the century. Horlicks, Ovaltine and other malted drinks were also popular as evening beverages.

๛ DECEMBER ๛

| 10 |
| 11 |
| 12 |
| 13 |
| 14 |
| 15 |
| 16 |

∾ D E C E M B E R ∾

17

18

19

20

21

22

23

MAKING A CLEAN SWEEP

Brooms and brushes were often home-made from hogs' bristles, birch twigs or heather, but sturdy broom heads were also available from the ironmonger's store. Mops were made from woollen rags and were used for cleaning floors and fire-places.

In opulent houses, household floors were often sanded before being swept, and in less grand houses sand was kept on the kitchen floor and stairs all the time to soak up grease, mud and dirt. The sand was brought to the door by special hawkers called "sandmen" and it was spread in a thick covering over the entire floor. Patterns were often marked in the sand to give a decorative effect. Sand was also used for scouring pots and pans.

Stone-flagged, brick and earthenware floors usually had no covering, although coconut matting was sometimes used in wealthier houses. After it had been thoroughly scrubbed, the plain floor was sometimes decorated with patterns made with special soft stones or juices from plant leaves: brownstone, naturally occurring hyper-oxide of manganese, gave a brown stain; donkey-stone was white; ruddle-stone gave a rich, orange colour; and blue mould was a chalky substance that added a blue tone.

Once a week the hearth and front step were whitened with hearthstone (in the cities the step was whitened every day). It was believed that evil spirits could not cross the threshold of a house protected by such whiteness.

ELIZA ACTON'S CHRISTMAS PUDDING

INGREDIENTS

3 oz of flour
3 oz of breadcrumbs
6 oz of suet
6 oz of stoned raisins
6 oz of currants
4 oz of minced apples
5 oz of sugar
2 oz of candied peel
½ teaspoonful of spice
a few grains of salt
a small wine-glassful of brandy
3 eggs

This recipe is from Eliza Acton's *Modern Cookery*, 1868, in which it appears as "The Author's Christmas Pudding".

Mix and beat these ingredients well together, tie them tightly in a thickly-floured cloth, and boil them for three hours and a half. We can recommend this as a remarkably light small rich pudding; it may be served with German sauce, wine sauce or punch sauce.

Note: "spice" here probably means a mixture of mace, cinnamon and nutmeg. We would use a proprietary blend of mixed spice today.

STIRRUP SUNDAY

The traditional day for making Christmas
pudding ready for December 25th was
Advent Sunday (also called Stirrup
Sunday) which fell on or near November
25th. The pudding mixture was stirred
by every member of the family in
descending order of seniority, and it was
most important to stir in a clockwise
direction with a wooden spoon. Each
person wished three times, although
only one of the wishes would be
granted. In large houses the kitchen staff
would prepare all the ingredients for the
pudding; and the children, if not the
whole family, would go down into the
kitchen to join in the ritual. The pudding
was then boiled in a linen cloth. This
was well floured on the inside to
prevent the mixture from seeping out
during the cooking process. The
pudding was served with one of a variety
of sauces – brandy sauce, vanilla custard
or one of the three mentioned in the
recipe. German sauce was made with
sherry, sugar, egg yolks and lemon juice;
wine sauce was made with a mixture of
lemon or orange rind, sugar, water,
butter, flour and sherry, port, madeira or
white wine; punch sauce was made with
lemon rind, sugar, water, butter and
flour and brandy, white wine, rum and
orange juice.

Left, for those who did not have the
services of a cook, a ready-made
pudding was available from Peek, Frean
and Co.

∾ D E C E M B E R ∾

24
25
26
27
28
29
30

JACOB'S CREAM CRACKERS

Commercially produced biscuits became popular in the eighteenth century when sailors were given supplies of ship's biscuits. By the 1840s fancy sweet biscuits were becoming available. Mr Huntley and Mr Palmer began with a hand-baking operation, but quickly developed a production sequence which helped meet the huge demand from the public. In 1865, Peak Frean invented the "pearl biscuit" which was light, gave a good number to the pound and therefore gave excellent value for money. Jacob's Cream Crackers were launched in 1875 by William Beale Jacob at the family factory in Ireland. The recipe was based on the American cracker but with extra fat "creamed" into the flour to make it less dry. Biscuits were usually supplied in tin-lined wooden boxes and were sold loose by grocers. Some, however, appeared in smaller packets or tins, and would have been a familiar sight in Victorian store cupboards.

Peak Frean produced a wide range of sweet and savoury biscuits, including Bourbon, Nice and Twiglets.

JACOB & Cᴼˢ

ORIGINAL & BEST

CREAM CRACKERS

THE LAUNDRY ROOMS

Most large houses had a separate ironing and drying room next to the bleaching house. In it would be housed the mangle, clothes-horses for drying and airing, and sometimes airing cupboards heated by hot water pipes or a special furnace. There would be a large pine, or deal, ironing table that was covered with a thick, woollen blanket and a calico ironing sheet. Smaller and specially shaped boards were used for shirt fronts, sleeves, caps and collars. As well as the ordinary flat- or box-iron, the laundries might also have had a range of specialized irons: the glossing iron was used for polishing starched linens and cottons; a small lace, or Italian, iron was for crimping and finishing fine lace edges, frills or bows; a sleeve-iron (also called a flounce or ox-tongue iron) helped to smooth fabric high up into pleats and sleeves; an egg-iron was used for finishing the tops of sleeves or gathered waist bands; and crimping frames and goffering irons were used to produce a tighter, finer effect on narrow pleats, caps, collars, cuffs and ruffles.

If the laundress scorched the linens, stains could be removed with a mixture of fuller's earth, vinegar, dried fowl's dung, soap and onion juice.

The bases of flat irons were often coated with beeswax or soap to make them glide more easily over the linens.

∽ D E C · J A N ∽

31

1

2

3

4

5

6

CONVERSION OF MEASUREMENTS FOR AMERICAN AND METRIC EQUIVALENTS:

VICTORIAN SHERRY TRIFLE (page 21)
1 pint/600 ml/2½ cups double (heavy)
   cream
3 oz/75 g/6 tbsp sugar
1 pint/600 ml/2½ cups custard
2 oz/50 g/½ cup sweet almonds
½ pint/300 ml/1¼ cups sherry

EASTER CAKE (page 34)
¾ lb/350 g/3 cups plain (cake) flour
8 oz/225 g/1 cup butter
5 oz/150 g/⅔ cup superfine sugar
3 oz/75 g/just under 1 cup currants

CURRANT AND RASPBERRY ICE CREAM
(page 79)
1 lb/450 g/2½ cups redcurrants
½ lb/225 g/1⅓ cups raspberries
10 oz/275 g/1¼ cups sugar
1 pint/600 ml/2½ cups double (heavy)
   cream

MINCED MUTTON (page 107)
1 oz/30 g/2 tbsp butter
1 oz/25g/¼ cup plain (cake) flour

ELIZA ACTON'S CHRISTMAS PUDDING
(page 114)
3 oz/75 g/¾ cup plain (cake) flour
3 oz/75 g/¾ cup breadcrumbs
3 oz/75 g/½ cup shredded suet
6 oz/175 g/just under 1 cup raisins
6 oz/175 g/just under 1 cup currants
4 oz/100 g/just under ½ cup minced
   apples
5 oz/150 g/⅔ cup sugar
2 oz/50 g/⅓ cup candied peel

PICTURE ACKNOWLEDGEMENTS

The author and the publisher would like to thank the following for permission to reproduce illustrations and photographs in this book: Bodleian Library, Oxford: pp 12, 24, 39, 51, 52, 53, 54, 61, 65, 71, 78, 81, 83, 84, 104 106, 110, 117. Bridgeman Art Library: pp 19, 37, 58, 91, 101, 118. Mary Evans Picture Library: pp 9, 11, 15, 16, 22, 28, 44, 46, 56, 62, 82, 88 (and cover). Fine Art Photographic Library Ltd: pp 7, 27, 43, 76, 87, 109, 113. The Hulton-Deutsch Collection: p 67. Illustrated London News Picture Library: pp 115. The Robert Opie Collection: pp 3, 5, 31, 34, 40, 41, 48, 49, 57, 72, 74, 75, 84, 92, 97, 110, 114, 116. University of Reading, Institute of Agricultural History and Museum of English Rural Life: pp 68, 95, 98.

   The hand-marbled paper for the cover was created by Ann Muir Marbling and supplied by Falkiner Fine Papers Ltd, London.

෨෨෨෨